FUTURE DIARY

FUTURE DIARY

BY

MARK
VICTOR
HANSEN

CAROL
FOREMAN
BROCKFIELD

EDITOR

SHOWCASE
PUBLISHING
COMPANY

FAIRFIELD
CALIFORNIA

Photography by
Jaren Dahlstrom, John Pearson,
Richard Stacks, Susan Katz
and Terrence Toole

Designed by Paul Hobson, San Francisco

Showcase Publishing Company
3422 Astoria Circle
Fairfield, California 94533

Distributed to the retail trade by
Elsevier-Dutton Publishing Company, Inc.
New York

Library of Congress Catalog No. 80-51759

ISBN 0-88205-226-8

Printed in the
United States of America

TABLE
OF
CONTENTS

FUTURE DIARY is a guide to planning your future. What shape will your future take? Unless you decide that question now, circumstance will decide it for you.

FUTURE DIARY presents concepts which will make you a strong believer in yourself. It puts you in touch with your true desires, gives you an awareness of your true needs.

FUTURE DIARY initiates meaningful conversations with your inner self. It will be your blueprint for a course of action that will lead you to success of your own choosing.

Deciding your life agenda is your first critical priority.

You can do extraordinary things when you have extraordinary things planned to do.

This diary is composed not of yesterday's events or today's events, but of *tomorrow's* events. This is a diary of tomorrow and the day after that and the year after that.

FUTURE DIARY brings your future into the present tense of your life. The moment you inscribe your desires in this diary they begin to move toward you. *They are reality already awaiting your arrival . . .*

This
is the
FUTURE DIARY
of

_____

Seeing myself as a success,
feeling myself as a success,
believing in my success,
I am success.

Personalized goals must be stated in the first person:
I AM. I AM is your self-definition in process. We instantly
and constantly contract with ourselves to become
whatever we attach to the words I AM. Write everything
good that you are and want to be.

Affirmation:
The words you say to yourself
or others say to you
that you think about
and act upon
and that ultimately
act upon you.

Give yourself positive affirmations.

I am a happy person
I am a loyal and true friend
I am a nurturing parent
I am an inspired artist
I am a dynamic executive

Etch the thought
into the fabric of your being
until you become it.

Restate your goals in the second person: YOU ARE.
Add to your list.

You are a happy person
You are a loyal and true friend
You are a terrific thinker
You are responsible for your life

The world's conditioning
is so complete
that we must spend half our lives
unlearning what we have learned,
reprogramming ourselves
for what *we want to know.*

We are influenced by what we hear others say about
us – "YOU ARE." Nine out of ten of these inputs are
denials or negatives. You are erasing them now.

Give yourself more positive affirmations
beginning with YOU ARE.

Your future emanates totally and absolutely from your present mental attitude.

Restate your goals in the third person, using your full name. Repeat them aloud early in the morning and late at night. Reiterate twice daily for one month.

Man is what he believes.
Anton Chekov (1860-1904)

Expand your goals in the third person.
Reiterate three times daily for a month and fill all the inner
spaces of your thoughts, feelings, and nature.

Show me a thoroughly satisfied man
and I will show you a failure.

Thomas Alva Edison (1847-1931)

Write down every good thing you want to be, do, or have.

Goals are a preview
of future events
and experiences
in your life.

Write down your dreams.

I want to operate a successful business
I want to grow spiritually every day of my life
I want to live in a house by the ocean
I want to love and be loved

Y̶ou have 18 billion brain cells
waiting to be activated
by a big goal.

Dream, fantasize, and expect your ideas to come into being.

It's not that people
want too much,
it's that they want
too little.

Begin by listing three tangible goals and three intangible goals.

Thinking is what life
is all about.
The most important thing
you can think about
is your life.

Write down your hopes, plans, aspirations,
and high purposes.

When you know clearly
what you want
you'll get it with
accelerating acceleration.

Your potential is limitless. Continue to expand this list.

When you know clearly
what you want
you'll wake up every morning
excited about life.

Add to this list every day.
Reach for the sky!

Describing your desires
on these pages
is the initial step
to their physical
realization.

Attain your desires by picturing them keenly, clearly,
crisply in your mind. Write a detailed description
of your major goals.

Dedicate yourself
to the good you deserve
and desire for yourself.
Give yourself peace of mind.
You deserve to be happy.

Write a minutely detailed description of your primary goal.
See it in your mind's eye as if it is already yours.
Can you visualize it? Can you feel it?

Dreams are the
touchstones
of our characters.

Henry David Thoreau (1817-1862)

Select another goal to materialize in your mind's eye.

Principle:
Ideas are always created
as forms.

Turn your ideas into reality.

Time is a priority.
We all invest it wisely
when we are on purpose
when we are dedicated
to the business
of accomplishing our lives.

Consider your economic wants:
whole life
next ten years
next five years
this year
this week
today

We can do all things
if we will.

Leon Battista Alberti (1404-1472)

Consider your spiritual wants:
whole life
next ten years
next five years
this year
this week
today

A man who dares
to waste one hour of time
has not discovered
the value of life.

Charles Darwin (1809-1882)

Write the names of the people you love. Include mentors,
people with tremendous capabilities and knowledge which
they are willing to share — people you would like to
imitate, emulate, match, and surpass.

We have no greater
or lesser conquest
than over ourselves.

Leonardo da Vinci (1452-1519)

There is no growth in life without the development
of one's own unique self. Write:

how I want to grow
mentally
physically
emotionally
spiritually

W e are
what we think about.

Give yourself time limitations that see you to these
achievements. Then set new ones.

books I will read
audio-tapes I will hear
music I will listen to
speakers I will experience
courses I will take

Μy interest is in the future because I am going to spend the rest of my life there.

Charles F. Kettering (1876-1958)

my desired weight
my desired measurements
my daily exercise program
my diet
my sleep regimen
playtime

He who asks of life nothing but
the improvement of his own nature . . .
is less liable than anyone else
to miss and waste life.
Henri Frederic Amiel (1821-1881)

to accept my feelings
to develop courage
to offer understanding to others

Every thought
in the subconscious is created;
ultimately it demonstrates itself.

prayer
meditation
church attendance
believing in myself

There is only one success –
to be able to spend your life
in your own way.

Christopher Morley (1870-1957)

Qualify these goals and set a schedule for accomplishing them.

becoming more effective
developing contacts
securing a promotion

If a man takes no thought
about what is distant,
he will find sorrow near at hand.
Confucius (c.551-479 B.C.)

Quantify goals in these areas and set a
schedule for accomplishing them.

income
savings
investments
tithing
projects

Time goes, you say?
Ah no,
alas, time stays,
we go.
Austin Dobson (1840-1921)

Schedule time to spend with your family. Make this
priority time.

house chores
leisure activities
shared time with mate
shared time with children
shared time with parents

Every man is worth
just so much
as the things are worth
about which he busies himself.

Marcus Aurelius (A.D. 121-180)

people to meet
people to get to know
keeping in touch
entertaining

Future is creative stuff
that can be constructed
as we like it.
It only requires
predrawn blueprints
so that you can make your way
smooth, beautiful, and perfect.

Consider:

*How can I increase my sowing
(service, giving, productivity) and
my reaping (receiving, rewards, harvest)*

The only waste
of human resources
is to let them go unused.

Consider:

What have I to give out of love of selfless giving
to myself
to my family
to my work
to my church
to my community
to the world

Reflect . . .
grow . . .
plan . . .
enjoy . . .
experience
a life renaissance.

Let this list grow day by day.
four things I am thankful for today

M ay you live all the days
of your life.

Jonathon Swift (1667-1745)

Each day add four more things you are thankful for.

And in today already walks tomorrow.
Samuel Taylor Coleridge (1772-1834)

Review this list from time to time. Let it nourish you.

Destiny is not a matter of chance,
it is a matter of choice;
it is not a thing to be waited for,
it is a thing to be achieved.

William Jennings Bryan (1860-1925)

You ought to be afraid to die
until you've contributed
something great
back to humanity.

Oliver Wendell Holmes (1809-1894)

FUTURE DIARY
takes you
from the future
to the present.

Visualize these successes clearly in your mind's eye.

The more you think about it the quicker you get it.

Can you taste these successes?

Life is a series of collisions with the future;
it is not the sum of what we have been
but what we yearn to be.

Jose Ortega y Gasset (1883-1955)

Write down your goals as if they have already been
accomplished, giving dates.

In 1985 I inspired an audience of 10,000
In 1986 I bought a red Rolls Royce

If you write
a big enough personal agenda
you will help
all of mankind.
Does the bumblebee know
the vast scope of its job
as it pollinates a flower?

Change your thoughts
and you
change your world.